A to Z
baby poetry

Written by Colleen Reding Mearn
Illustrated by E.S. Dolan Dix

Bauer Books

For Mike and Biz
- Colleen Reding Mearn

For Lawson and Waverly
- E.S. Dolan Dix

Bauer Books
San Francisco, CA

First published in the United States of America, 2021

Editor: Erika Nichols-Frazer

Bauer Books is an independent publishing house dedicated to bringing joy and adventure to
children and parents everywhere. We believe in the power of community, shared stories, and
quality time together.

ISBN 978-0-578-92273-7

Follow along with Bauer Books and tag us in your family book selfies on Instagram
@Bauer_Books!

Am

When someone asks me how I am, I send a pic of you.
I guess it's not an answer, but still it is so true.
I've lost myself and found myself, a paradox it seems.
I'm happy, then I'm sad; I live in the extremes.
I think about my former life and how I was so free.
Then marvel at how every choice has led you here to me.

Baby

I miss you when I'm sleeping. So much, I stay awake.
I think of how you hold my hand; it's more than I can take.
Or how you turn your head, when you're being shy.
And grin from ear to ear when we hold you up to fly.
But as you grow, I surely see my baby slip away.
So give me one more moment here— push off another day.

Clear

You've arrived! You're here! We've been waiting for you.
There are packages, visitors- such hullabaloo!
So what's all the fuss about one tiny bean?
Such a small bundle stealing the scene.
The purpose of life is clear to us now,
To take care of you the best we know how.

Dream

Watching you sleep is our new favorite thing.
Eyes flutter, lips smile, and sometimes you sing.
There's one thing we wonder, so please let us know.
Do you dream, little one? And of what, if so?

Ending

I think you like this book a lot- it's quite clear to see.
Your eyes light up, you calm right down, and fold up into me.
But you've eaten every corner, and the pages all need mending.
I used to like it too, my dear, but I can't read the ending.

Follow

Let us show you the world, at least what we know.
It isn't that much, you'll learn as you grow.
We'll follow your lead if you just take my hand.
There's so much to learn, explore, understand.
We've lived and we've loved, now we'll do it through you.
But better this time, since we'll have your view.

Grandparents

A grandparent's love is a thing to behold.
And "no" is a word that you'll never be told.
They'll rock you, they'll hug you, they'll read you good books.
They'll hold you and tell you you've got their good looks.

Heart

Here on my chest, you lay down your head.
I know not forever, which fills me with dread.
Your heart locks with mine- in tandem, we beat.

      Bum-bum,

            bum-bum,

                  Bum-bum…

                        Repeat.

Inch

I can do nothing else when you're sleeping on me.
No emails, no chores, no brushing my teeth.
I can't move an inch for my now-cold tea.
But trust me, there's no place that I'd rather be.

Journey

You'll scoot then you'll crawl, you'll walk and then run.
If you skipped any part, we'd miss half the fun.
Remember this, love, as you journey on through.
That life's in the small steps of all that you do.

Know

Can you kiss baby's lips? Will this rash go away?
Babies get acne? Is it here to stay?
When you whimper at night, what does it mean?
Will the worrying end? When you're eighteen?
The more that we look, the less that we know.
So let's stop the search and learn as we go.

Little

That I would love you, I already knew.
What's surprised me the most is who else would too.
Your aunts, cousins, and friends far away-
Aren't faking it, love, you brighten their day.
With one tiny smile, you remind us all
To love all the little things, no matter how small.

Mystery

Arms in or arms out? To rock or to sway?
As soon as we learn, you change anyway.
To stroll or be carried, please give us a clue.
Will you smile with strangers or stare as you do?
You're a mystery to us, you plague us with doubt.
One of these days will we figure you out?

Never

Never is a word I never want you to know.
Oops- there I've said it, now please let it go.
You can be who you choose and do as you please.
You can go join a circus, try flying trapeze.
You can climb mountains in faraway lands,
Or stay close to home and make art with your hands.
Whoever you are, please don't forget
That never's a word to not ever accept.

Outside

We put on real pants, and we took you outside.
Might not seem like much, but we're bursting with pride.
You weigh less than a snowball and sleep all day long,
You sound easy on paper; that's really so wrong.
You cried the whole time, and I nearly did too.
Let's do it again! But not for a few.

Pout

You're precious, you're perfect. We can't get enough.
From your sweet rolly neck to your hair's little tuft.
You sneeze and we melt; you laugh, we obsess.
When you're sad, dear, let's face it. We're frankly a mess.
If ever our love for you is in doubt,
Look at my face when you give us a pout.

Quirks

You'll wave with one hand, but not with the other.
And sneak out your arms when you're under cover.
You'll nap in my lap with your head facing down,
But not sleep at all the other way 'round.
You're so new to this world, so how can this be?
These quirks that you came with...They aren't from me!

Ruffle

Ruffle butt bottoms and too-big sunnies,
Bear ear beanies and booties with bunnies.
Baby clothes really are strange and quite silly.
But 'til you can stop me, you're pleated and frilly.

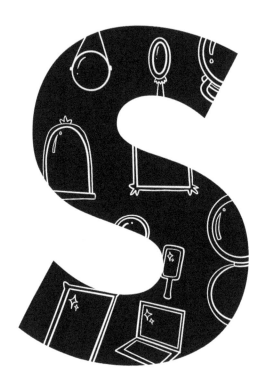

Stare

Look at that baby, just over there.
They've got your lashes, your cheeks, and even your stare.
They move when you move, and you smile in delight.
With you and your mirror friend, it's love at first sight!

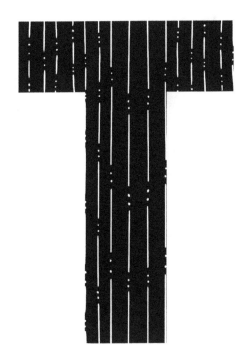

Tiny

Stay little, we say, though we know it can't be.
Tiny hands, tiny toes, so perfect to me.
But each day you grow, showing more who you are:
Our new favorite version of you, by far.

Undone

I know this is crazy, but listen to me.
When you sleep, I hover, to feel you breathe.
You're fine, I'm sure! So safe in your crib.
I'm sorry, I know - I'm obsessed with you, kid!
Just give me a sign, and I'll slink away.
A snortle or sigh, and I'm A-OK!
Undone by this love, there is no doubt.
Phew! All is good, I can hear you breathe out!

View

Swish swish swish, whoosh whoosh whoosh, please go to sleep...
There's so much to do, don't make a peep!
The dishes need washing, there's crust in my hair.
I can't seem to find clean clothes anywhere!
But now that the day has bid you adieu,
I'll linger a while, and view photos of you!

Who

Who do you look like? Is a game that we play.
Your grandma? Your uncle? Your aunt in some way?
If only you could, you'd say "I'm just me!"
And of course, you're unique- I do guarantee.
But if I'm being honest, shhh, so no one else hears.
I dare say I do think you might have my ears.

X

"X" marks the spot for the treasure, they say.
Where rubies, diamonds, and emeralds all lay.
Gold may be shiny and silver is nice,
But you are the one thing without a price.
I'd trade all the treasure across the land
For a moment of you just holding my hand.

You

Adorable, Bubbly, and Cuddly, too.

Dramatic, Endearing, and Fun through and through.

Gorgeous, Happy, Inspired- Just the best.

Kind, Loving, Magnificent, Not like the rest.

Observant, Precious, and Quite a good baby.

Rosy and Sweet, Truly perfect to me.

Unequivocally Vibrant, and so nice and Wiggly.

There's an X-factor too- You're Zany and giggly.

You're A to Z awesome, too good to be true.

You're more than we hoped for just being YOU.

Zoo

Good stretch, my darling, you're greeting the day.
I admire your spirit- Let's eat, sleep, and play!
(I could have slept more, but, hey- that's OK.)
There's no time to lose, there is so much to see.
We'll bundle you up, and you'll stay close to me.
We'll head to the park, then stroll to the zoo!
I'll show you the world, as you sleep on through.

About the Author and Illustrator

Colleen Reding Mearn

Colleen Reding Mearn lives in San Francisco with her husband and Little Biz. She works in tech policy by day and enjoys rhyming with her baby at night. She graduated from Georgetown University in 2010 and the Harvard Graduate School of Education in 2016. She grew up in Mt. Prospect, IL where her parents instilled in her a lifelong love of books and where she had the good fortune of meeting the very talented E.S. Dolan Dix!

Visit her on instagram @Bauer_Books.

E.S. Dolan Dix

E.S. Dolan Dix lives in Los Angeles, CA where she gets to spend her days drawing up strange creatures, brave superheroes, and adorable letters for her pals. She is the author and illustrator of "Henri Wilson Decides to Do Something" and a series of activity books designed to help build confidence and self-love. She also grew up in Mount Prospect where most of her time was spent in a pool, reading, or scooping ice cream next to her brilliant friend Colleen.

Visit her online at www.ESDolanDix.com.

CPSIA information can be obtained
at www.ICGtesting.com
Printed in the USA
BVHW050728031121
620551BV00003B/561